USBORNE
LATIN
WORDS
STICKER BOOK

Jonathan Sheikh-Miller

Illustrated by Stephen Cartwright

Designed by Tom Lalonde
Latin consultant: Anne Dicks

About 3,000 years ago, a people called the Latins founded a cluster of villages on the banks of the River Tiber in Italy. These villages grew into the great and powerful city of Rome, which became the hub of a vast empire, stretching from Britain to North Africa. Wherever they went, the Romans built roads and cities, and introduced their way of life and their language: Latin.

The city of Rome

Rome itself was a magnificent city – with paved streets and running water, as well as grand palaces, temples, bathhouses and archways. Cities all over the empire were based on Rome. At the heart of each one was a large open space called a forum, where market traders set up their stalls and people gathered to meet their friends.

turba (f)

templum (n)

fenestra (f)

bibliotheca (f) rus (n) ignis (m)

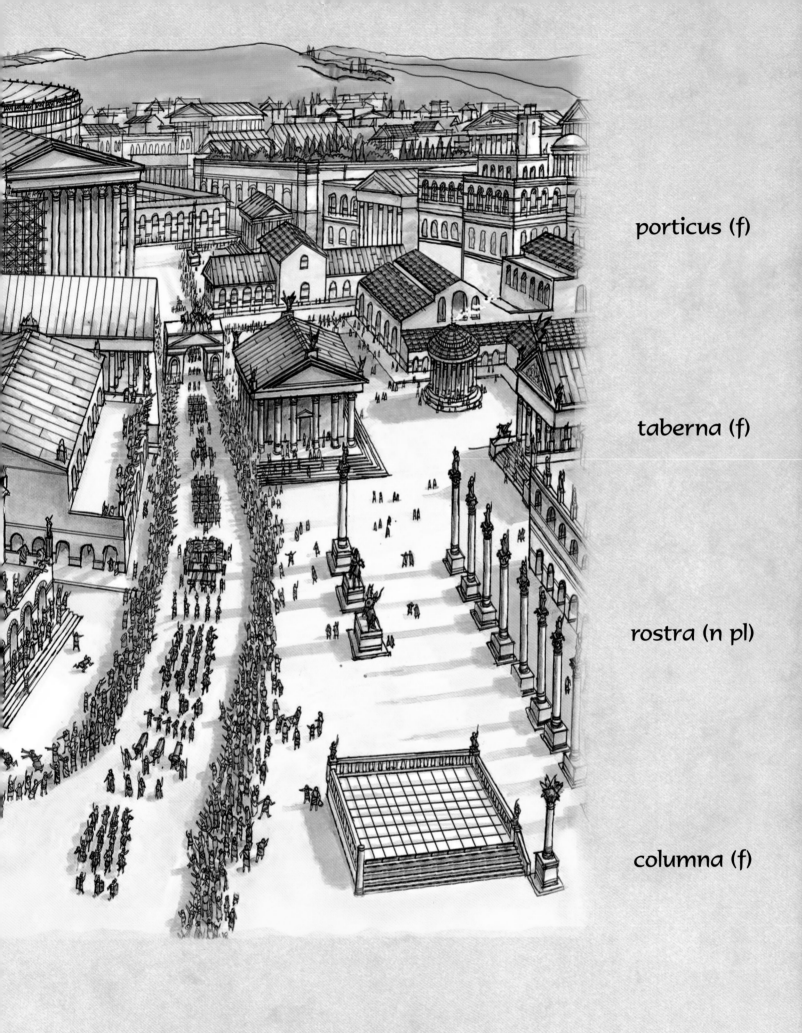

porticus (f)

taberna (f)

rostra (n pl)

columna (f)

forum (n)
arcus (m)
funus (n)

3

On the road

The Romans built a network of roads all over their empire. They always chose the shortest, straightest, flattest route possible – so that they could move their armies quickly to distant parts of the empire. Their roads were built to last – even today many European roads follow the routes of old Roman ones.

plaustrum (n)

collis (m)

nuntius (m)

flumen (n)

saxum (n)

ager (m)

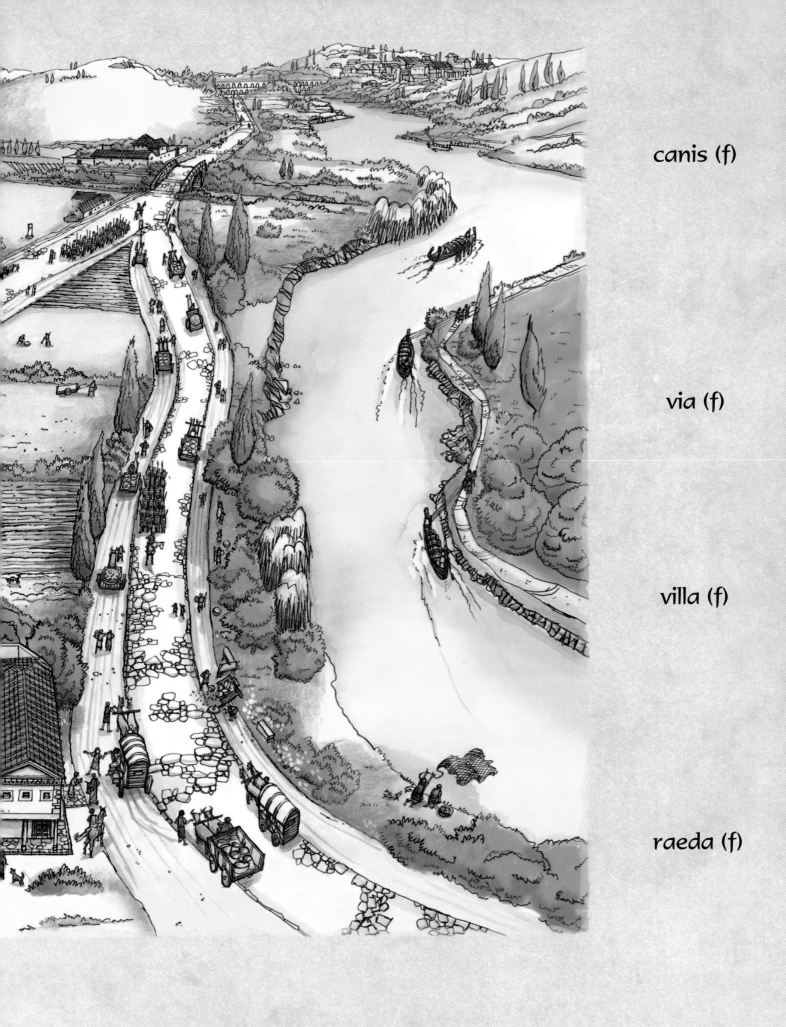

canis (f)

via (f)

villa (f)

raeda (f)

domus (f)   bos (m, f)   urbs (f)

At home

Most Romans lived in apartments, but a few families were rich enough to afford a large, comfortable house of their own. Most houses had one floor – or two, if you were very rich. They were built around an open courtyard, or atrium, with a pool in the middle.

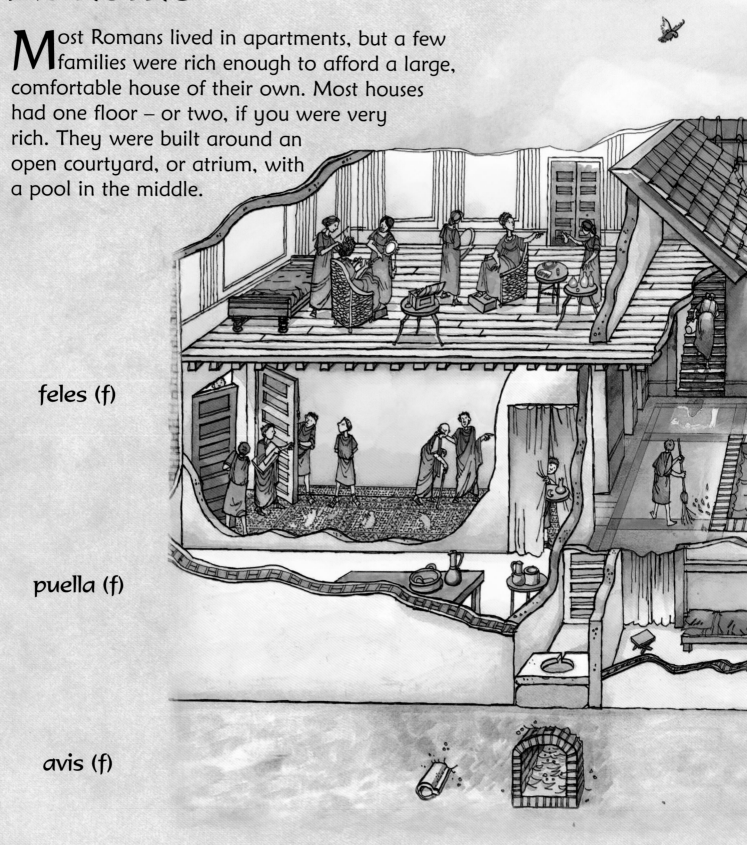

feles (f)

puella (f)

avis (f)

cubiculum (n)

folium (n)

impluvium (n)

cloaca (f)

arca (f)

lararium (n)

latrina (f)

The walls of this house
have been cut away
so you can see inside.

senex (m)   mensa (f)   femina (f)

A Roman feast

Wealthy Romans loved to entertain their friends with extravagant banquets. The guests lay on couches to eat, with musicians playing, while servants brought in dish after dish. There were sometimes as many as seven courses, and parties could last until the early hours of the morning.

vinum (n)

pomum (n)

servus (m)

barba (f)

culter (m)

patella (f)

impluvium (n)
rainwater pool

mensa (f)
table

arcus (m)
arch

nuntius (m)
messenger

anser (m)
goose

miles (m)
soldier

libum (n)
cake

tectum (n)
roof

fenestra (f)
window

servus (m)
slave

turba (f)
crowd

arbor (f)
tree

homo (n)
man

cubiculum (n)
bedroom

ager (m)
field

castra (n pl)
camp

plaustrum (n)
cart

saxum (n)
stone

apodyterium (n)
changing room

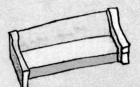
sella (f)
bench

equus (m)
horse

folium (n)
leaf

culter (m)
knife

urbs (f)
city

canis (f)
dog

hortus (m)
garden

pomum (n)
fruit

feles (f)
cat

patella (f)
plate

mons (m)
mountain

statua (f)
statue

scriba (m)
secretary

domus (f)
house

ripa (f)
river bank

avis (f)
bird

eques (m)
cavalryman

via (f)
road

vitis (f)
grapevine

athleta (m/f)
wrestler

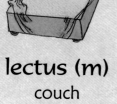
lectus (m)
couch

lararium (n)
household altar

lignum (n)
log

malum (n)
apple

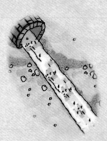
aqua (f)
water

templum (n)
temple

senex (m)
old man

scalae (f pl)
ladder

calathus (m)
basket

villa (f)
country house

fur (m)
thief

vinum (n)
wine

rus (n)
countryside

porticus (f)
colonnade

signum (n)
standard

raeda (f)
carriage

bos (m, f)
ox

rostra (n pl)
platform

caldarium (n)
hot room

vestimenta (n pl)
clothes

latrina (f)
toilet

forum (n)
market

pons (m)
bridge

poeta (m)
poet

hasta (f)
spear

funus (n)
funeral procession

navis (f)
ship

femina (f)
woman

puer (m)
boy

stabulum (n)
stable

cibus (m)
food

flumen (n)
river

bibliotheca (f)
library

captivus (m)
prisoner

arca (f)
chest

arx (f)
citadel

lucerna (f)
oil lamp

fons (m)
fountain

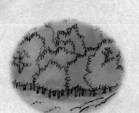

silva (f)
wood

ignis (m)
fire

scutum (n)
shield

lana (f)
wool

collis (m)
hill

cloaca (f)
drain

puella (f)
girl

cratera (f)
mixing bowl

ianua (f)
door

hospes (m)
guest

columna (f)
column

piscina (f)
swimming pool

barba (f)
beard

taberna (f)
shop

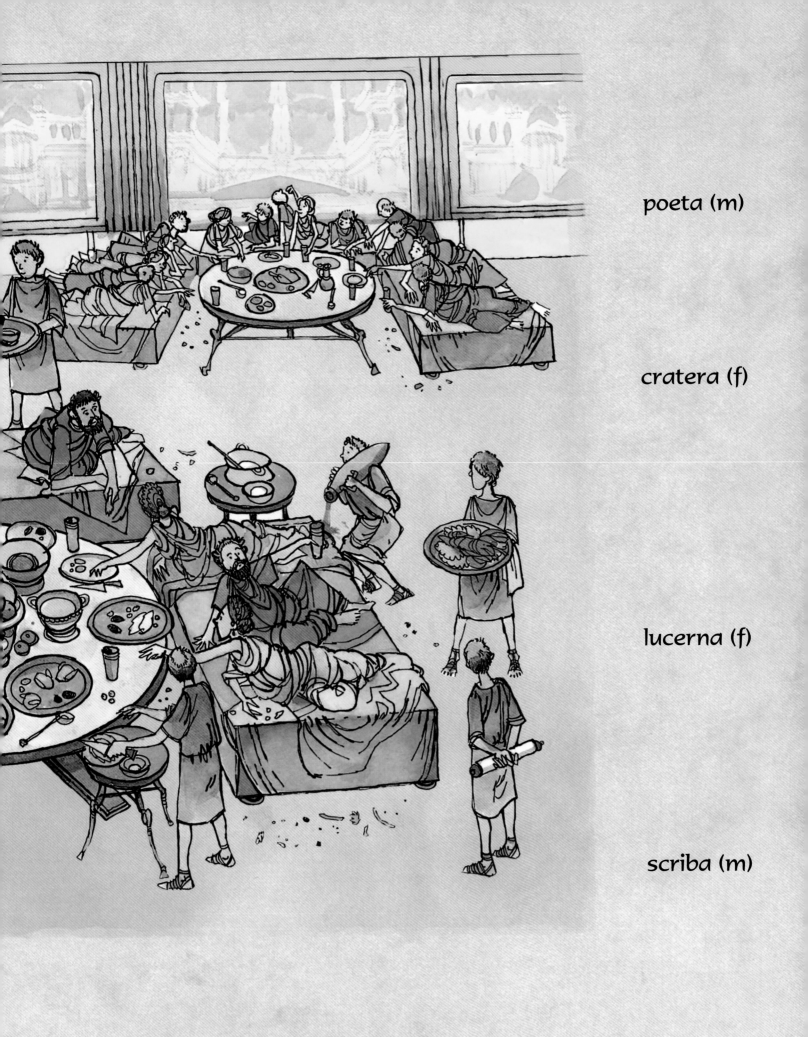

poeta (m)

cratera (f)

lucerna (f)

scriba (m)

cibus (m)   hospes (m)   lectus (m)

9

At the baths

Roman bathhouses were a very special institution. Every town had at least one – and in Rome there were eleven. Each one had warm pools, cool pools and piping hot steam pools. All Romans, rich or poor, went regularly. But it wasn't just somewhere to wash or swim – it was a great place to meet friends and hear the latest gossip.

fur (m)

lignum (n)

fons (m)

apodyterium (n)   libum (n)   athleta (m / f)

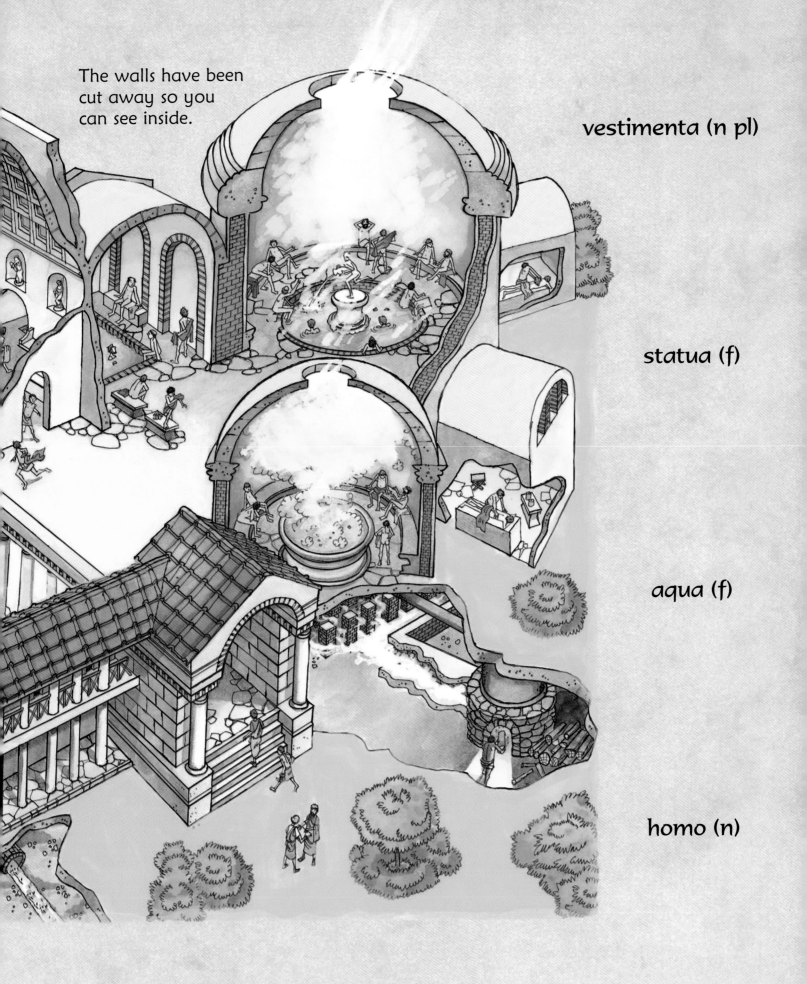

The walls have been cut away so you can see inside.

vestimenta (n pl)

statua (f)

aqua (f)

homo (n)

piscina (f)

sella (f)

caldarium (n)

11

In the countryside

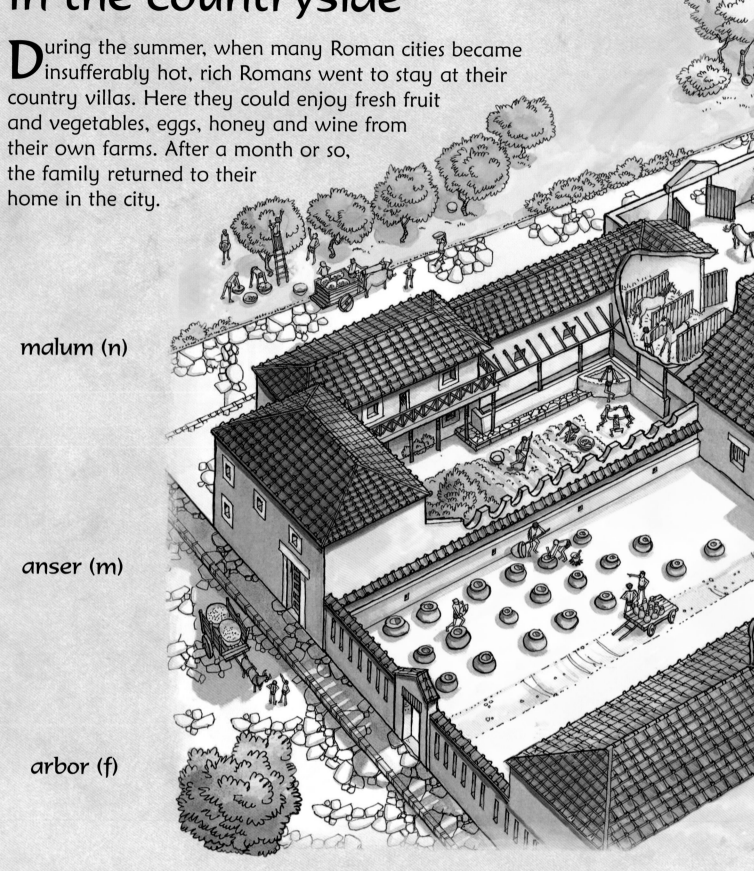

During the summer, when many Roman cities became insufferably hot, rich Romans went to stay at their country villas. Here they could enjoy fresh fruit and vegetables, eggs, honey and wine from their own farms. After a month or so, the family returned to their home in the city.

malum (n)

anser (m)

arbor (f)

vitis (f)   hortus (m)   equus (m)

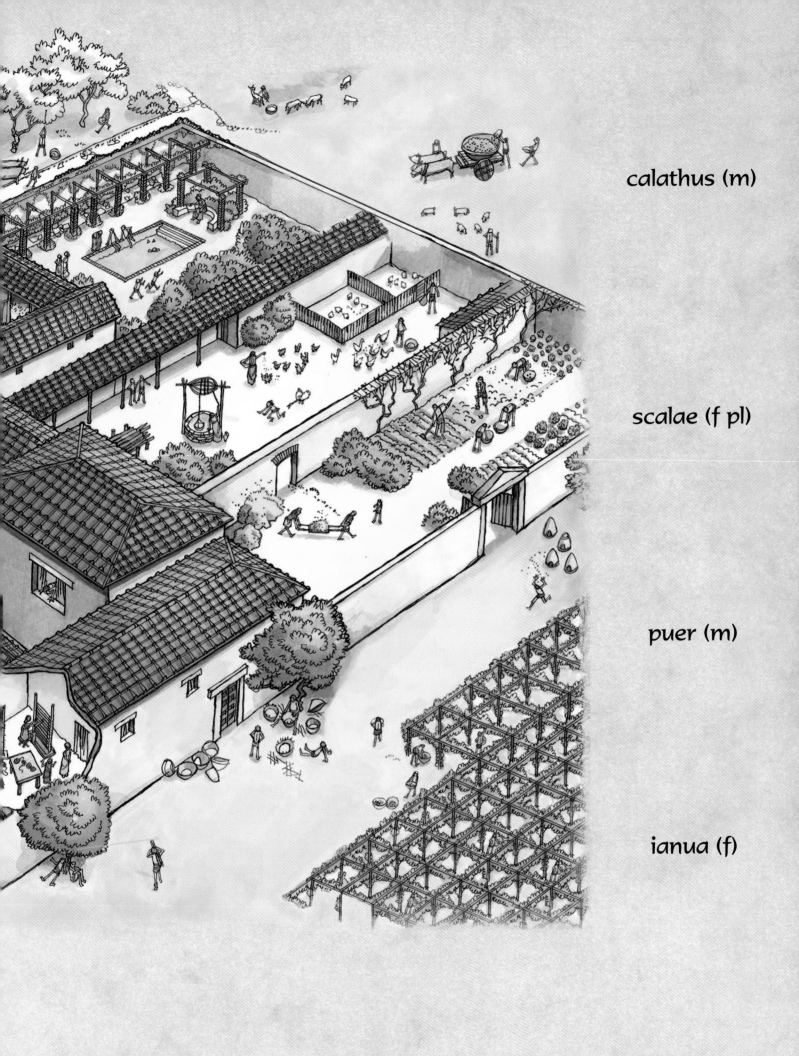

calathus (m)

scalae (f pl)

puer (m)

ianua (f)

lana (f)   tectum (n)   stabulum (n)

13

The army on campaign

The Roman army was one of the most successful and feared fighting forces in history - without it the empire would never have existed. But army life was tough. To conquer new land and attack enemies on their borders, soldiers had to march vast distances carrying all their equipment. Then they had to build a camp.

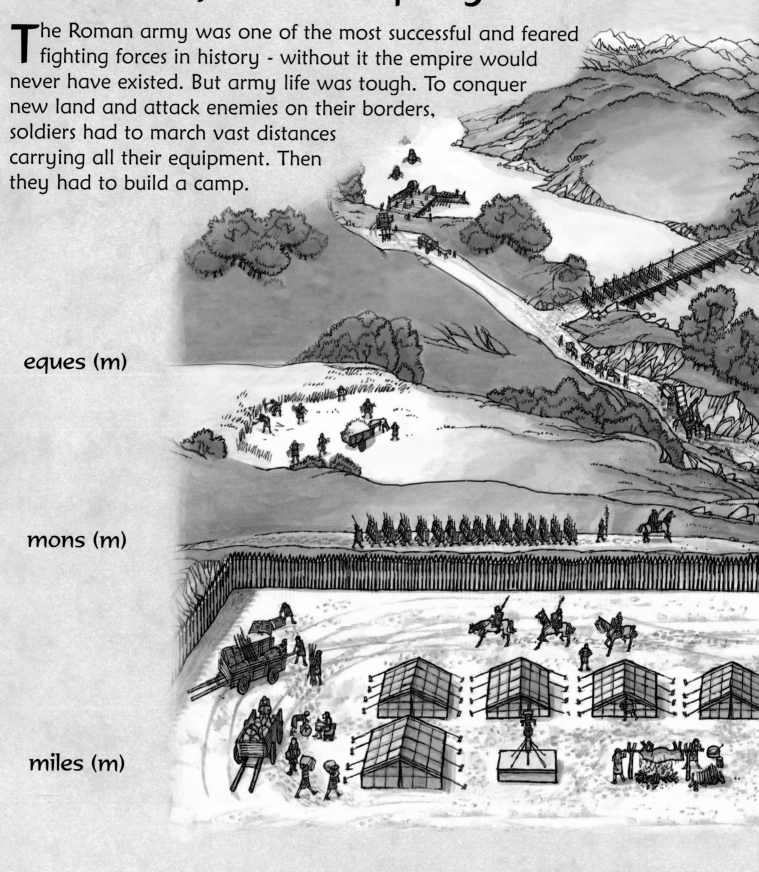

eques (m)

mons (m)

miles (m)

ripa (f)   castra (n pl)   captivus (m)

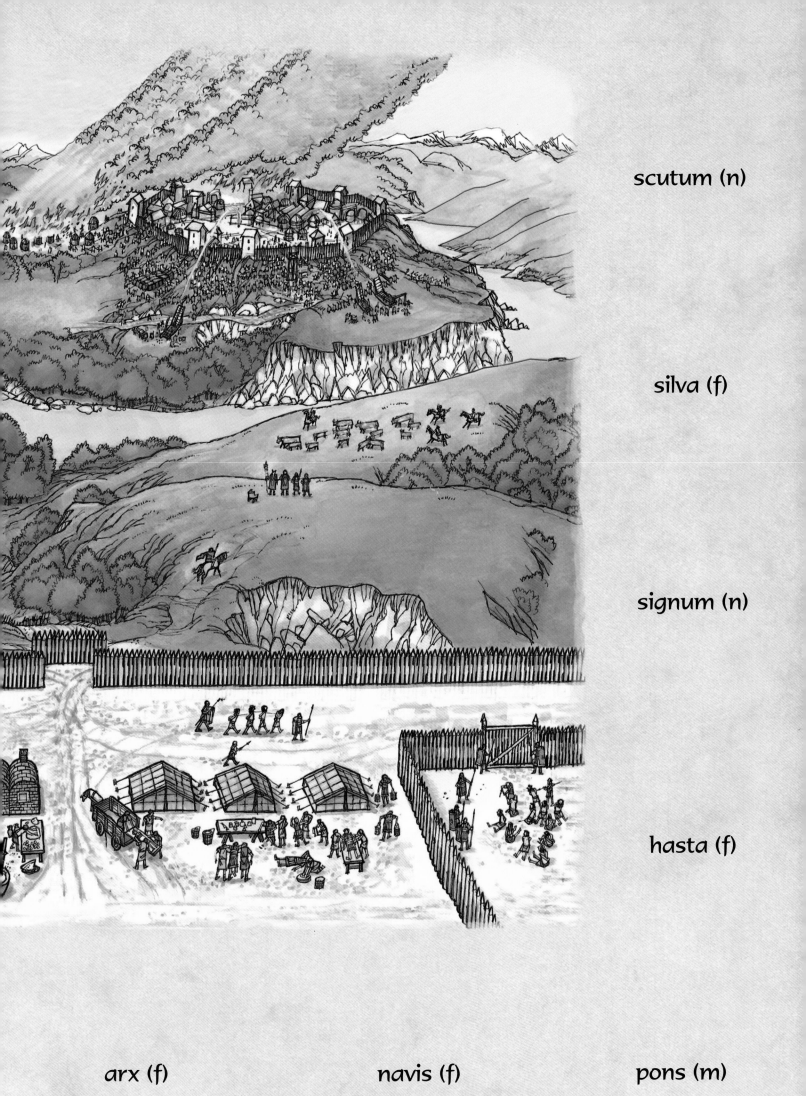

scutum (n)

silva (f)

signum (n)

hasta (f)

arx (f)　　　　　navis (f)　　　　pons (m)

Latin words

Nouns

All Latin nouns are either masculine, feminine or neuter (neither). This is called their gender. The gender is shown in the word list by the letters m, f and n. Many masculine nouns end in -us, feminine nouns in -a and neuter nouns in -um. But there are many exceptions and many other endings too. A few words are found only in the plural, just like the English words "trousers" and "scissors".

Pronunciation

Nobody knows exactly what Latin sounded like when the Ancient Romans spoke it. Today, Latin is pronounced slightly differently in different parts of the world. In English-speaking countries, the letters are normally pronounced just as you would expect. There are a few exceptions: "c" is usually pronounced "k", "v" is usually pronounced "w", and "i" before a vowel at the beginning of a word is pronounced "y". For example, ianua is pronounced "yanua". Every letter is pronounced, even "e" at the end of a word, and it can be fun to make "r" sound more dramatic than it does in English!

Vowel sounds

A long line printed above some vowels shows that the sound is heavy, or long:

ā = ah
ē = ay (as in "hay")
ī = ee
ō = or
ū = oo

When speaking Latin, it is usual to stress the first syllable (part) of the word. With longer words, the next-to-the-last syllable, or the one before it, is stressed instead: whichever feels more comfortable.

ager (m)	field
ānser (m)	goose
apodytērium (n)	changing room
aqua (f)	water
arbor (f)	tree
arca (f)	chest
arcus (m)	arch
arx (f)	citadel
āthlēta (m/f)	wrestler
avis (f)	bird
barba (f)	beard
bibliothēca (f)	library
bōs (m/f)	ox
calathus (m)	basket
caldārium (n)	hot room
canis (f)	dog
captīvus (m)	prisoner
castra (n pl)	camp
cibus (m)	food
cloāca (f)	drain
collis (m)	hill
columna (f)	column
crātēra (f)	mixing bowl
cubiculum (n)	bedroom
culter (m)	knife
domus (f)	house
eques (m)	cavalryman
equus (m)	horse
fēlēs (f)	cat
fēmina (f)	woman
fenestra (f)	window
flūmen (n)	river
folium (n)	leaf
fōns (m)	fountain
forum (n)	market
fūnus (n)	funeral procession
fūr (m)	thief
hasta (f)	spear
homō (m)	man
hortus (m)	garden
hospes (m)	guest
iānua (f)	door
ignis (m)	fire
impluvium (n)	rainwater pool
lāna (f)	wool
larārium (n)	household altar
lātrīna (f)	toilet
lectus (m)	couch
libum (n)	cake
lignum (n)	log
lucerna (f)	oil lamp
mālum (n)	apple
mēnsa (f)	table
mīles (m)	soldier
mōns (m)	mountain
nāvis (f)	ship
nūntius (m)	messenger
patella (f)	plate
piscīna (f)	swimming pool
plaustrum (n)	cart
poēta (m)	poet
pōmum (n)	fruit
pōns (m)	bridge
porticus	colonnade
puella (f)	girl
puer (m)	boy
raeda (f)	carriage
rīpa (f)	bank (of river)
rōstra (n pl)	platform
rūs (n)	countryside
saxum (n)	stone
scālae (f pl)	ladder
scrība (m)	secretary
scūtum (n)	shield
sella (f)	bench
senex (m)	old man
servus (m)	slave
signum (n)	standard
silva (f)	wood
stabulum (n)	stable
statua (f)	statue
taberna (f)	shop
tēctum (n)	roof
templum (n)	temple
turba (f)	crowd
urbs (f)	city
vestīmenta (n pl)	clothes
via (f)	road
vīlla (f)	country house
vīnum (n)	wine
vītis (f)	grapevine